HANGMAN

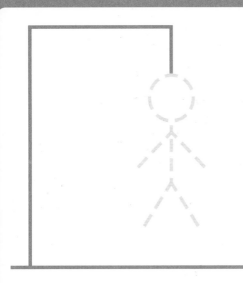

Fill in letters as they are guessed.

ABCDEFGHIJK
NOPQRSTUVWXYZ

HANGMAN

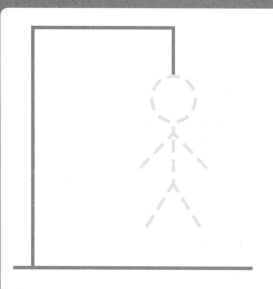

Fill in letters as they are guessed.

A B C D E F G H I J K L M
N O P Q R S T U V W X Y Z

HANGMAN

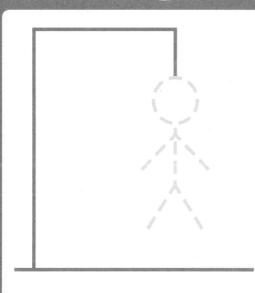

Fill in letters as they are guessed.

A B C D E F G H I J K L M
N O P Q R S T U V W X Y Z

HANGMAN

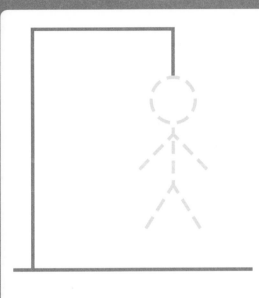

Fill in letters as they are guessed.

A B C D E F G H I J K L M
N O P Q R S T U V W X Y Z

HANGMAN

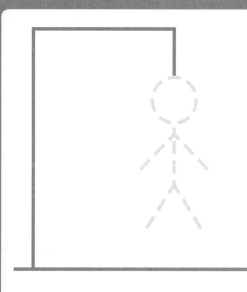

Fill in letters as they are guessed.

A B C D E F G H I J K L M
N O P Q R S T U V W X Y Z

HANGMAN

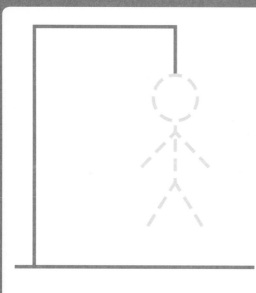

Fill in letters as they are guessed.

ABCDEFGHIJKLM
NOPQRSTUVWXYZ

HANGMAN

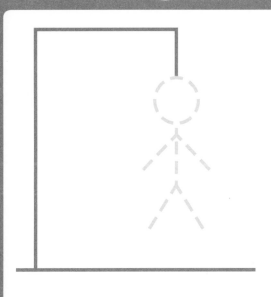

Fill in letters as they are guessed.

ABCDEFGHIJKLM
NOPQRSTUVWXYZ

HANGMAN

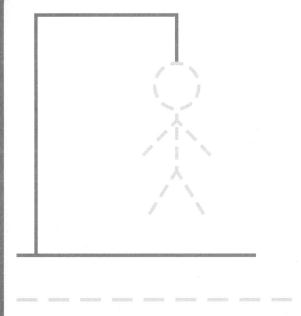

Fill in letters as they are guessed.

ABCDEFGHIJKLM
NOPQRSTUVWXYZ

HANGMAN

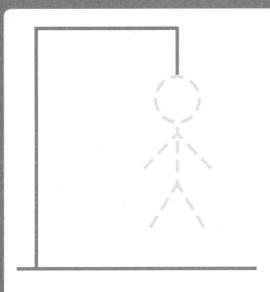

Fill in letters as they are guessed.

ABCDEFGHIJKLM
NOPQRSTUVWXYZ

HANGMAN

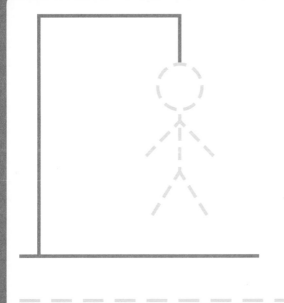

Fill in letters as they are guessed.

A B C D E F G H I J K L M
N O P Q R S T U V W X Y Z

HANGMAN

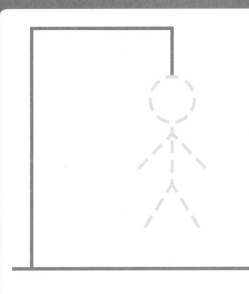

Fill in letters as they are guessed.

A B C D E F G H I J K L M
N O P Q R S T U V W X Y Z

HANGMAN

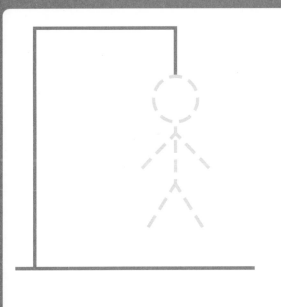

Fill in letters as they are guessed.

ABCDEFGHIJKLM
NOPQRSTUVWXYZ

HANGMAN

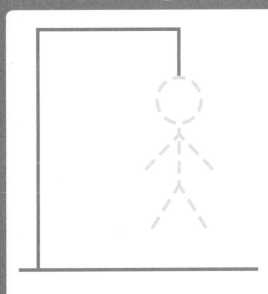

Fill in letters as they are guessed.

A B C D E F G H I J K L M
N O P Q R S T U V W X Y Z

HANGMAN

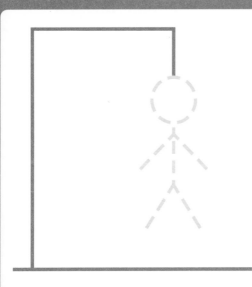

Fill in letters as they are guessed.

ABCDEFGHIJKLM
NOPQRSTUVWXYZ

HANGMAN

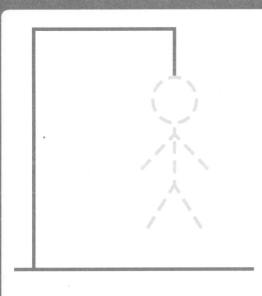

Fill in letters as they are guessed.

A B C D E F G H I J K L M
N O P Q R S T U V W X Y Z

DOTS & BOXES

DOTS & BOXES

DOTS & BOXES

DOTS & BOXES

DOTS & BOXES

DOTS & BOXES

DOTS & BOXES

DOTS & BOXES

DOTS & BOXES

DOTS & BOXES

DOTS & BOXES

DOTS & BOXES

DOTS & BOXES

DOTS & BOXES

DOTS & BOXES

OUT AND ABOUT BINGO

COFFEE HOUSE

CELL PHONE

BABY

SKYLINE

DOG

CLOUD

HEADPHONES

MAGAZINE

NEWSPAPER

BOTTLED WATER

BILLBOARD

SPEED SIGN

CAR

REST AREA

MOTORCYCLE

BRIDGE

BUS

SATELLITE DISH

LAKE

FLAG

TRAFFIC CONE

OUT OF STATE

GAS STATION

FOREST

POLICE CAR

OUT AND ABOUT BINGO

COFFEE HOUSE	CELL PHONE	BABY	SKYLINE	DOG
CLOUD	HEADPHONES	MAGAZINE	NEWSPAPER	BOTTLED WATER
BILLBOARD	SPEED SIGN	CAR	REST AREA	MOTORCYCLE
BRIDGE	BUS	SATELLITE DISH	LAKE	FLAG
TRAFFIC CONE	OUT OF STATE	GAS STATION	FOREST	POLICE CAR

OUT AND ABOUT BINGO

 COFFEE HOUSE	 CELL PHONE	 BABY	 SKYLINE	 DOG
 CLOUD	 HEADPHONES	 MAGAZINE	 NEWSPAPER	 BOTTLED WATER
 BILLBOARD	 SPEED SIGN	 CAR	 REST AREA	 MOTORCYCLE
 BRIDGE	 BUS	 SATELLITE DISH	 LAKE	 FLAG
 TRAFFIC CONE	 OUT OF STATE	 GAS STATION	 FOREST	 POLICE CAR

OUT AND ABOUT BINGO

COFFEE HOUSE	CELL PHONE	BABY	SKYLINE	DOG
CLOUD	HEADPHONES	MAGAZINE	NEWSPAPER	BOTTLED WATER
BILLBOARD	SPEED SIGN	CAR	REST AREA	MOTORCYCLE
BRIDGE	BUS	SATELLITE DISH	LAKE	FLAG
TRAFFIC CONE	OUT OF STATE	GAS STATION	FOREST	POLICE CAR

OUT AND ABOUT BINGO

COFFEE HOUSE	CELL PHONE	BABY	SKYLINE	DOG
CLOUD	HEADPHONES	MAGAZINE	NEWSPAPER	BOTTLED WATER
BILLBOARD	SPEED SIGN	CAR	REST AREA	MOTORCYCLE
BRIDGE	BUS	SATELLITE DISH	LAKE	FLAG
TRAFFIC CONE	OUT OF STATE	GAS STATION	FOREST	POLICE CAR

OUT AND ABOUT BINGO

COFFEE HOUSE	**CELL PHONE**	**BABY**	**SKYLINE**	**DOG**
CLOUD	**HEADPHONES**	**MAGAZINE**	**NEWSPAPER**	**BOTTLED WATER**
BILLBOARD	**SPEED SIGN**	**CAR**	**REST AREA**	**MOTORCYCLE**
BRIDGE	**BUS**	**SATELLITE DISH**	**LAKE**	**FLAG**
TRAFFIC CONE	**OUT OF STATE**	**GAS STATION**	**FOREST**	**POLICE CAR**

OUT AND ABOUT BINGO

COFFEE HOUSE	CELL PHONE	BABY	SKYLINE	DOG
CLOUD	HEADPHONES	MAGAZINE	NEWSPAPER	BOTTLED WATER
BILLBOARD	SPEED SIGN	CAR	REST AREA	MOTORCYCLE
BRIDGE	BUS	SATELLITE DISH	LAKE	FLAG
TRAFFIC CONE	OUT OF STATE	GAS STATION	FOREST	POLICE CAR

OUT AND ABOUT BINGO

 COFFEE HOUSE	 CELL PHONE	 BABY	 SKYLINE	 DOG
 CLOUD	 HEADPHONES	 MAGAZINE	 NEWSPAPER	 BOTTLED WATER
 BILLBOARD	 SPEED SIGN	 CAR	 REST AREA	 MOTORCYCLE
 BRIDGE	 BUS	 SATELLITE DISH	 LAKE	 FLAG
 TRAFFIC CONE	 OUT OF STATE	 GAS STATION	 FOREST	 POLICE CAR

OUT AND ABOUT BINGO

COFFEE HOUSE	CELL PHONE	BABY	SKYLINE	DOG
CLOUD	HEADPHONES	MAGAZINE	NEWSPAPER	BOTTLED WATER
BILLBOARD	SPEED SIGN	CAR	REST AREA	MOTORCYCLE
BRIDGE	BUS	SATELLITE DISH	LAKE	FLAG
TRAFFIC CONE	OUT OF STATE	GAS STATION	FOREST	POLICE CAR

OUT AND ABOUT BINGO

COFFEE HOUSE	CELL PHONE	BABY	SKYLINE	DOG
CLOUD	HEADPHONES	MAGAZINE	NEWSPAPER	BOTTLED WATER
BILLBOARD	SPEED SIGN	CAR	REST AREA	MOTORCYCLE
BRIDGE	BUS	SATELLITE DISH	LAKE	FLAG
TRAFFIC CONE	OUT OF STATE	GAS STATION	FOREST	POLICE CAR

OUT AND ABOUT BINGO

COFFEE HOUSE	**CELL PHONE**	**BABY**	**SKYLINE**	**DOG**
CLOUD	**HEADPHONES**	**MAGAZINE**	**NEWSPAPER**	**BOTTLED WATER**
BILLBOARD	**SPEED SIGN**	**CAR**	**REST AREA**	**MOTORCYCLE**
BRIDGE	**BUS**	**SATELLITE DISH**	**LAKE**	**FLAG**
TRAFFIC CONE	**OUT OF STATE**	**GAS STATION**	**FOREST**	**POLICE CAR**

OUT AND ABOUT BINGO

 COFFEE HOUSE

 CELL PHONE

 BABY

 SKYLINE

 DOG

 CLOUD

 HEADPHONES

 MAGAZINE

 NEWSPAPER

 BOTTLED WATER

 BILLBOARD

 SPEED SIGN

 CAR

 REST AREA

 MOTORCYCLE

 BRIDGE

 BUS

 SATELLITE DISH

 LAKE

 FLAG

 TRAFFIC CONE

 OUT OF STATE

 GAS STATION

 FOREST

 POLICE CAR

KNOCKKNOCKSTUFF.COM • © 2015 KNOCK KNOCK LLC

OUT AND ABOUT BINGO

COFFEE HOUSE	CELL PHONE	BABY	SKYLINE	DOG
CLOUD	HEADPHONES	MAGAZINE	NEWSPAPER	BOTTLED WATER
BILLBOARD	SPEED SIGN	CAR	REST AREA	MOTORCYCLE
BRIDGE	BUS	SATELLITE DISH	LAKE	FLAG
TRAFFIC CONE	OUT OF STATE	GAS STATION	FOREST	POLICE CAR

OUT AND ABOUT BINGO

COFFEE HOUSE	CELL PHONE	BABY	SKYLINE	DOG
CLOUD	HEADPHONES	MAGAZINE	NEWSPAPER	BOTTLED WATER
BILLBOARD	SPEED SIGN	CAR	REST AREA	MOTORCYCLE
BRIDGE	BUS	SATELLITE DISH	LAKE	FLAG
TRAFFIC CONE	OUT OF STATE	GAS STATION	FOREST	POLICE CAR

OUT AND ABOUT BINGO

COFFEE HOUSE	**CELL PHONE**	**BABY**	**SKYLINE**	**DOG**
CLOUD	**HEADPHONES**	**MAGAZINE**	**NEWSPAPER**	**BOTTLED WATER**
BILLBOARD	**SPEED SIGN**	**CAR**	**REST AREA**	**MOTORCYCLE**
BRIDGE	**BUS**	**SATELLITE DISH**	**LAKE**	**FLAG**
TRAFFIC CONE	**OUT OF STATE**	**GAS STATION**	**FOREST**	**POLICE CAR**